The GAMBOLS
BOOK Nº 18
by Dobs + Barry Appleby

CARTOONS SELECTED FROM
THE DAILY EXPRESS AND
THE SUNDAY EXPRESS

We took two young nieces out to lunch—they started with prawn cocktails which was their favourite. Then they had roast chicken with all the trimmings, and when we asked them what they wanted to follow they said 'prawn cocktail'. 'But', we said, 'you've already had prawn cocktail—now you should have an ice or something from the trolley'.

No—they wanted prawn cocktail. Of course we wouldn't let them have it—we explained that you can't finish a meal on prawn cocktails, and reluctantly they settled for strawberries and cream.

Afterwards we wondered to ourselves—why couldn't they have finished their meal with prawn cocktails?

GEORGE LOVES HIS FOOD BUT GAYE KEEPS A VERY STRICT EYE ON HIS WEIGHT

© 1968 Dobs + Barry Appleby

HAVE YOU NOTICED
HOW TIRED HUSBANDS
GET WHEN THEIR WIVES
WANT THEM TO GO OUT ?

WHEN OUR YOUNG NEPHEW AND NIECE
COME TO STAY THEY PLAY ALL SORTS OF
TRICKS ON US — BUT WE LOVE IT

THIS WAS THE CLANGER OF THE YEAR — WE HAD MORE LETTERS POINTING OUT THIS MISTAKE THAN ANY OTHER WE HAVE EVER MADE

PLUMBERS! I SUPPOSE THAT IT'S INEVITABLE THAT EVEN THE BEST OF THEM SHOULD MAKE A MESS

WE WERE INVITED TO A WEDDING AND TURNED UP A DAY TOO SOON! WE THOUGHT THAT WE HAD GONE TO THE WRONG CHURCH SO WE WENT ROUND TO THE BRIDE'S HOUSE AND FINISHED UP CUTTING SANDWICHES FOR THE RECEPTION!

AND THAT'S WHERE THE IDEA FOR THIS CARTOON CAME FROM

THE FASHION SENSATION OF THE YEAR
— GEORGE LOVES IT — BUT NOT ON GAYE
WHEN UNEXPECTED VISITORS CALL

GEORGE LOVES FISHING — HE FINDS IT
SO RESTFUL

SUNDAY HAS ALWAYS BEEN GEORGE'S FAVOURITE DAY — THERE'S SO MUCH MORE TIME TO READ THE SUNDAY EXPRESS — FROM WHICH THE FOLLOWING CARTOONS HAVE BEEN SELECTED

423

424

413

399

433

409

402

There *must* be a very large number of students studying Sociology, and I have a shrewd guess that they have recently been given the task of writing a thesis on Comic Strips, because we have been inundated with requests from students for help. And not only from students in this country.

Here is a typical letter:

"Dear Sir,

As I want to study the comic strip as a memoir of sociology and want to search after its deep lying origin rather than to wander into a devious interpretation. I ask you therefore for the deep genuine meaning of your work.

Perhaps could you tell me its genesis and your conception of the characters. What meaning do you attach to the fact that the characters are an archetypal suburban couple? Could you let me know your particular vision of the characters and of the themes dealt with.

Your answers will help me to apprehend your work more faithfully and to avoid ridiculous exegesis.

Yours sincerely,"

Well when we'd worked out what that meant, we wrote a long and serious reply to each and every student. In other words we did their work for them.

And the interesting point is that, not one has written to say 'thank you'—so much for sociology.

406

418

426

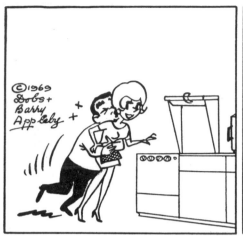

427

428

434

436

396

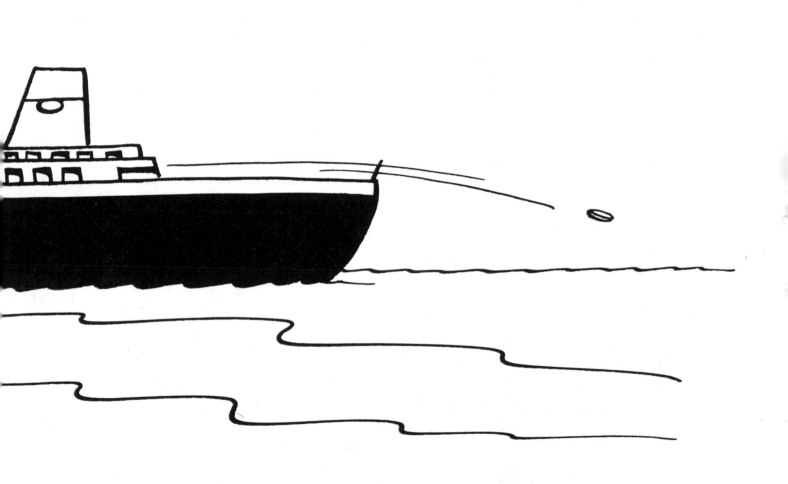

WHY IS IT THAT THE
TELEPHONE ALWAYS RINGS
JUST AS WE'RE ABOUT
TO HAVE A MEAL?

GAYE FINDS IT DIFFICULT ENOUGH TO BALANCE HER ACCOUNTS AS IT IS NOW BUT SHE DREADS TO THINK WHAT IT WILL BE LIKE IN DECIMALS

HOW MANY WIVES THINK LIKE THIS?

8-11

AND HOW MANY ARE 'TAKEN IN' BY THIS SORT OF OFFER?

OF COURSE, THIS IS GEORGE'S IDEAL SOLUTION TO ALL BILLS

'BYE 'BYE FOR NOW BUT WE'LL LOOK FORWARD TO SEEING YOU IN THE MORNING IN THE DAILY EXPRESS AND ON SUNDAY IN THE SUNDAY EXPRESS

Published by Beaverbrook Newspapers Limited, Fleet Street, London, E.C.4
and printed by H. Howes & Co., Ltd., Romford, Essex
© 1969 Barry Appleby